The Poetry Teatime Companion: A Brave Writer Sampler of British and American Poems
© 2016 by Julie (Bogart) Sweeney

Published by Brave Writer Press, West Chester, Ohio 45069

Website: www.bravewriter.com

ISBN-10: 0-9962427-7-5
ISBN-13: 978-0-9962427-7-6

Printed in the United States of America.
Library of Congress Catalog Card Number Pending

Supervising Editor: Julie Bogart
Series Editor: Nancy Graham

Image Curator: Jeannette Hall
Cover Photograph and Image Editor: Alli Parfenov
Typesetter/Designer: Sara McAllister

CONTENTS

WINTER

SOLITUDE

SPRING

© Julie (Bogart) Sweeney | bravewriter.com | poetryteatime.com

CREATURES OF LAND AND WATER

SUMMER

LIGHT BEARERS

ACKNOWLEDGMENTS

FOREWORD

Ah…it's Poetry Teatime. The delicious pause, the anticipation of tasty treats, the music of delightful language, and happy eager children. Put the kettle on, set the table, choose your tea, and begin. Let the magic of tea and poetry cast a spell on your family!

When I began the poetry teatime adventure with my own children, I never knew it would reach thousands of families. I simply saw an opportunity to create a love affair with language while sipping my favorite daily beverage: British tea.

At the time, I had been reading along on a homeschooling email list when the idea first took hold. One mother talked about reviewing geography terms with her children over tea. She shared this detail in a happenstance kind of way, but it caught my imagination! I knew immediately that I wanted to have tea with my children and learn at the same time, too!

My first opportunity came when Johannah, my daughter then 8 years old, showed interest in Shakespeare. I farmed out the other four children and set the table just for her: table cloth, tea cups, scones, little yogurt cups, and Leon Garfield's *Shakespeare Stories*. We sipped tea, lit candles, ate snacks, and I read to her the children's version of *A Midsummer Night's Dream*. The entire afternoon sparkled before us. Shakespeare's poetic language carried us away!

Gold! I immediately planned the next tea, and this time invited all five children to the table. I scattered poetry books and asked each child to select a poem to read. Even the non-readers picked poems by look on the page or illustration or simply because they could open the book!

We read, slurped, laughed, and ate our snacks. After 30 minutes had gone by, the energy waned in a satisfying way and we resumed the day's activities—only we did so with brighter spirits and happier faces. Poetry Teatime rapidly became the single best part of any day and a regular habit in the Bogart family.

Fast forward to adulthood: All five kids continue to drink tea and pair it with reading (whether books or poetry). In their corners of the globe, they've started Poetry Slam Meetings, written their own poetry, and have participated in the creation of literary magazines. They've hosted Poetry Teatimes in dorm rooms, for their homeschooled and public schooled friends, and whenever they come home to see me.

It is not an overstatement to say that Poetry Teatime has been the single most enjoyable, consistent homeschool activity of our lives. All the ways it has shaped our family connection, our love of language, and our appreciation for quality writing cannot be quantified. In short: we became closer to each other, and to the power of the English language—all while developing the habit of tea breaks (those necessary pauses in the hurry-scurry of life).

Poetry Teatimes work for two reasons: Parents believe in poetry (even if they fear it). Because they believe in poetry's intrinsic value, they are eager to create a space where poetry has a chance to be enjoyed and appreciated rather than dreaded or feared. Children, by contrast, believe in treats! They love a festive table, delicious snacks, and hot drinks! Poems are short, often funny, and satisfying to read aloud (poetry feels great in the mouth, just like brownies!). Together, parents and kids enter the experience convinced of its value. As a result, everyone wins!

This particular collection of poems came together as a serendipitous suggestion from Brave Writer team member: Nancy Graham. "Julie, does Brave Writer have a recommended collection of poems for Poetry Teatimes?" In a flash, I knew she had arrived at an inspired idea! I asked her to put together a list of classic, well-loved poems for our families to enjoy.

In the next month, Nancy set to the task with enthusiasm, rediscovering old favorites and categorizing them in happy ways. I read the first set of poems she sent me and found old friends already populating the pages—poems my kids had read and memorized as children. The collection evolved to its current state with notes and queries intended to create natural discussion between you and your kids.

Jeannette Hall, our intrepid curator of images, suggested we match pictures with each poem since children who can't yet read need a way to select their poems. The pairings immediately amplified the power of the poems and vice versa. Alli Parfenov, a friend of Brave Writer, professional photographer, and homeschooling mother created our cover photo and then transfigured the collected photographs into a "water-color look" that invites imagination, rather than stifling it. My sincere hope is that this little volume introduces your families to well known and beloved poems that have survived years of recitation.

Please also visit our wonderful website (poetryteatime.com) to discover resources to enhance your Poetry Teatimes.

Here's to the magical transport of tea and poems! May this collection lead you to new linguistic vistas and family intimacy!

Julie Bogart
Creator of Brave Writer
April 1, 2016

INTRODUCTION

By Nancy Graham

If you're new to Poetry Teatime, we're delighted that you are joining the thousands of Brave Writer families who have made a weekly habit of sharing tea and poetry. Poetry Teatime is a chance to slow down, savor the hour, and share the experience of being transformed by a little universe made up of words and your imagination. For more on preparing your teatime, download the Poetry Teatime Quick Start Guide on the home page of poetryteatime.com.

The Poetry Teatime Companion offers 52 poems to take you through the weeks of the year. Some are gathered and grouped by theme, others by season. We suggest you read these poems in any order you like—you might begin with shorter ones and move to longer ones, or browse through and choose at random or according to what grabs your attention. The 52 poets in these pages made significant contributions to English literature. Your children will encounter many of them again and again as they grow and continue to read.

Below are some tips for appreciating the poems you'll find in this companion. Take turns selecting them or choose them together. We invite you to get to know each one as if you have invited a new guest to your tea party. Greet it warmly, ask it questions, reread it several times. A poem can become the best of friends and the friendship will last a lifetime.

It will help you to have a dictionary handy. If possible, you might want to arrange for nearby Internet access as well, so you can look up unfamiliar ideas, words, images, or the poet's biographical details.

There are many ways to encounter a poem. Pick and choose the ones that give pleasure to you and your family.

Tips for Appreciating a Poem

Read the poem aloud.

Take turns reading the poem to the group. Some poems lend themselves to choral reading—saying together a refrain that repeats. Poetry Teatime is meant to be slow. Take a line and say it over and over. Read the poem through once and then pick through it, tasting a line at a time. Roll a word around on your tongue. Enjoy poems purely for the sound of them and let the meaning sink in slowly. Allow mysteries and puzzlements. Sit with them and enjoy the feeling of being affected by something you don't quite understand. A poem often reaches for something that is hard to fully grasp.

Sing the poem.

Poem, song, lyric, hymn—these are all names for what happens when we make music with words. The roots of the poems in this companion lie beneath the ruins of ancient Greece. Music and poetry have always been twins. Keeping this in mind opens a world of music for you to explore in tandem with poetry. Many of the poems in this collection were written to music or have been set to music. Examples can be found in the work of Robert Louis Stevenson, Robert Burns, and William Blake—and that's just for starters! If a poem strikes your fancy, poke around online or at the library and see if it's been set to music and recorded. This is a great way to learn poems by heart! Take the same idea in reverse: your children's best-loved song lyrics are poems, too. Read the lyrics and look at their use of language, rhythm, and rhyme.

Memorize the poem.

Even if it's not set to music, it's fairly easy to learn a short poem or a few lines from one. Memorized poems can be shared at family events, at bedtime, or when the mood strikes!

Think of the poem as a puzzle.

Poems use figurative language to help the reader view something from a different angle. Because of this, understanding a poem can be like unlocking a code or solving a puzzle. Enjoy this process and make it a game. Metaphor, simile, analogy—these are all ways that poems convey ideas or experiences in hidden ways.

Illustrate the poem.

Some poems have been beautifully illustrated by their authors or others. Examples of author-illustrators are William Blake, Oliver Herford, and of course, Beatrix Potter. Eugene Field's work was beautifully illustrated by Maxfield Parrish. Let teatime transition to art time and make some sketches based on the poem of the day.

Let the poem prompt your own.

Borrow a word, an image, a theme, a rhyme scheme, or a rhythm pattern and try your hand at writing your own poem. Take a line from a poem and use it to begin an "exquisite corpse." An exquisite corpse is a collective poem-making game made famous by the French Surrealists. Each person adds a line, then folds the paper so only one line is revealed to the next contributor. The results are usually zany. The first exquisite corpse gave the game its name—André Breton, the leader of the Surrealist movement, reported that this phrase resulted: "The exquisite corpse shall drink the new wine." Start with a line from a poem in this companion. The first player will add a line, then fold the paper so that only the next line is visible. The next player adds a line, covers the previous line, and passes it to the next player, and so on. Give it a try and read your exquisite corpse aloud!

Investigate further.

If someone in your family takes a liking to a poem in this companion, find the collection in which it was originally published and check it out! Get to know some of these poets in depth. Many of these poets wrote whole volumes of poetry for children. Some examples include Robert Louis Stevenson's *A Child's Garden of Verses*, Hilaire Belloc's *The Bad Child's Book of Beasts*, and Eugene Field's *Love-Songs of Childhood*. Look for more anthologies and collections based on your children's inclinations.

No doubt your teapot is well steeped by now. Without further ado — O! Hie thee to thine poem of the day!

Thank you for inviting Brave Writer to your tea party!

© Julie (Bogart) Sweeney | bravewriter.com | poetryteatime.com

Brave Writer

Brave Writer

FELLOW TRAVELERS

We begin our poetry companion with a series of poems about fellowship. A companion can be another human, an imaginary being, or something even harder to grasp—a song, a wooden shoe that takes you to sea, a star or a time of day, a special place or a refuge.

Journeys come in different disguises, too. When we move from one house to another, go on a trip, or take a hike, those journeys involve physical travel. When we go through steps to learn a new skill or change a habit, those are journeys of another kind.

Who are the "fellow travelers" in each poem? How would you describe their "journeys"?

Introduction to the Songs of Innocence

Piping down the valleys wild
Piping songs of pleasant glee
On a cloud I saw a child,
And he laughing said to me,

"Pipe a song about a Lamb";
So I piped with merry chear,
"Piper pipe that song again"—
So I piped, he wept to hear.

"Drop thy pipe thy happy pipe
Sing thy songs of happy chear";
So I sung the same again
While he wept with joy to hear.

"Piper sit thee down and write
In a book that all may read"—
So he vanish'd from my sight.
And I pluck'd a hollow reed,

And I made a rural pen,
And I stain'd the water clear,
And I wrote my happy songs
Every child may joy to hear.

—*William Blake*

• •

Born in 1757 in London, England, William Blake became not only one of the great poets of the English language, but one of the most original visual artists of his time. He studied engraving and illustrated his own and others' work—you can easily find his images online or at the library. The word "cheer," has an archaic spelling with an "a" in Blake's poem. Cheer comes from the Latin word for face and used to refer to any mood or frame of mind. Now we think of it as a happy mood.

How does the repetition of forms of the word "pipe" affect you as you read this poem? How would you tell the story of this poem in your own words?

• •

Wynken, Blynken, and Nod

Wynken, Blynken, and Nod one night
Sailed off in a wooden shoe —
Sailed on a river of crystal light
Into a sea of dew.
"Where are you going, and what do you wish?"
The old moon asked the three.
"We have come to fish for the herring-fish
That live in this beautiful sea;
Nets of silver and gold have we!"
Said Wynken,
Blynken,
And Nod.

The old moon laughed and sang a song,
As they rocked in the wooden shoe,
And the wind that sped them all night long
Ruffled the waves of dew.
The little stars were the herring-fish
That lived in the beautiful sea.
"Now cast your nets wherever you wish —
Never afeard are we!"
So cried the stars to the fishermen three,
Wynken,
Blynken,
And Nod.

All night long their nets they threw
To the stars in the twinkling foam —
Then down from the skies came the wooden shoe,
Bringing the fishermen home:
'Twas all so pretty a sail, it seemed
As if it could not be,
And some folk thought 'twas a dream they'd dreamed
Of sailing that beautiful sea —
But I shall name you the fishermen three:
Wynken,
Blynken,
And Nod.

Wynken and Blynken are two little eyes,
And Nod is a little head,
And the wooden shoe that sailed the skies
Is a wee one's trundle-bed.
So shut your eyes while Mother sings
Of wonderful sights that be,
And you shall see the beautiful things
As you rock in the misty sea,
Where the old shoe rocked the fishermen three: —
Wynken,
Blynken,
And Nod.

—*Eugene Field*

Eugene Field (1850-1895) wrote poems for children in addition to being a journalist and humorist. His father, Roswell Martin Field, became famous as the attorney for Dred Scott, who sued for his freedom from slavery. The artist Maxfield Parrish painted beautiful illustrations to accompany Field's work—look for them online or in a library. Relish the language and lilting rhythm of this beautiful bedtime poem as you read it aloud.

Brave Writer

The Arrow and the Song

I shot an arrow into the air,
It fell to earth, I knew not where;
For, so swiftly it flew, the sight
Could not follow it in its flight.

I breathed a song into the air,
It fell to earth, I knew not where;
For who has sight so keen and strong,
That it can follow the flight of song?

Long, long afterward, in an oak
I found the arrow, still unbroke;
And the song, from beginning to end,
I found again in the heart of a friend.

—Henry Wadsworth Longfellow

Henry Wadsworth Longfellow (1807-1882) is perhaps best known as the author of the poems "The Song of Hiawatha" and "Paul Revere's Ride." Born in Portland, Maine, Longfellow traveled to Europe after college to learn German, French, Spanish, and Italian. While teaching and directing the Modern Languages Department at Harvard University, he became popular enough to sustain himself full-time as a writer from the age of 47 on. This poem is notable for its rhymes—not just end rhymes (rhyming the final words of two or more lines), but you may find various internal rhymes as well (rhyming words within one or more lines). How many rhymes can you find in this poem?

An Hymn to the Morning

Attend my lays, ye ever honour'd nine,
Assist my labours, and my strains refine;
In smoothest numbers pour the notes along,
For bright Aurora now demands my song.
Aurora hail, and all the thousand dies,
Which deck thy progress through the vaulted skies:
The morn awakes, and wide extends her rays,
On ev'ry leaf the gentle zephyr plays;
Harmonious lays the feather'd race resume,
Dart the bright eye, and shake the painted plume.
Ye shady groves, your verdant gloom display

To shield your poet from the burning day:
Calliope awake the sacred lyre,
While thy fair sisters fan the pleasing fire:
The bow'rs, the gales, the variegated skies
In all their pleasures in my bosom rise.
See in the east th' illustrious king of day!
His rising radiance drives the shades away—
But Oh! I feel his fervid beams too strong,
And scarce begun, concludes th' abortive song.

—Phillis Wheatley

Born in Senegal, Phillis Wheatley (c.1753 – 1784) was kidnapped, transported to Boston, and sold into slavery. Homeschooled alongside the children of the Wheatleys, who purchased her to be their servant, she learned English, Greek, Latin, and read the Bible. At age 20, she became the first published African American poet.

One thing that makes poetry different from casual conversation is that poets achieve their effects by switching words around. (Sort of like Yoda: "Powerful you have become; the dark side I sense in you.") Sometimes "decoding" a line with switched-up syntax takes time. Some things that will help you decode this poem: A "lay" is a song. In the first few lines the poet is hoping for help from the Muses (the "honor'd nine") to write her poem. In Greek mythology, the nine Muses were goddesses who where in charge of the arts and sciences. Now you know where the word *museum* comes from! It's a special building devoted to one or more of the muses. Calliope is the muse of the writer. "Aurora" means dawn.

Who do you think the "king of day" could be? Can you translate a few lines of this poem into your own words?

Ozymandias

I met a traveller from an antique land,
Who said—"Two vast and trunkless legs of stone
Stand in the desert. . . . Near them, on the sand,
Half sunk a shattered visage lies, whose frown,
And wrinkled lip, and sneer of cold command,
Tell that its sculptor well those passions read
Which yet survive, stamped on these lifeless things,
The hand that mocked them, and the heart that fed;
And on the pedestal, these words appear:

My name is Ozymandias, King of Kings;
Look on my Works, ye Mighty, and despair!
Nothing beside remains. Round the decay
Of that colossal Wreck, boundless and bare
The lone and level sands stretch far away."

—*Percy Bysshe Shelley*

If you don't know Percy Bysshe Shelley (1792 – 1822) by name, you may have heard of the monster invented by his wife, Mary Shelley—who wrote the novel *Frankenstein*. Born in Broadbridge Heath, England, Shelley is one of the epic poets of the 19th century—that means they wrote poems about heroic deeds and adventures. In "Ozymandias," Shelley is using his description of the statue to comment on something else—he is making a metaphor. Aside from the statue, what do you think he is writing about in this poem?

This poem is a sonnet—a fourteen-line poem metered in iambic pentameter. Sometimes people describe iambic pentameter as sounding like a heartbeat: ba BUM ba BUM ba BUM ba BUM ba BUM. In iambic pentameter, there are five iambs, or heartbeats, for each line of poetry. See if you can read some of the lines of this poem with the heartbeat (ba BUM ba BUM rhythm) like this: I **MET** a **TRAV'**ler **FROM** an **AN**tique **LAND**. Sometimes the rhythm will shift a little at the beginning of the line, but in general, the heartbeat will hold throughout the poem. You'll see it again later in this collection. See if you can find all the poems written in iambs!

Ozymandias! What a great name. Did Shelley make it up? No! Ozymandias is another name for the 13th-century Egyptian Pharaoh, Rameses the Great. Shelley read about him in the work of a Greek historian named Diodorus Siculus. Whoa! Another amazing name.

Brave Writer

Up-Hill

Does the road wind up-hill all the way?
   Yes, to the very end.
Will the day's journey take the whole long day?
   From morn to night, my friend.

But is there for the night a resting-place?
   A roof for when the slow dark hours begin.
May not the darkness hide it from my face?
   You cannot miss that inn.

Shall I meet other wayfarers at night?
   Those who have gone before.
Then must I knock, or call when just in sight?
   They will not keep you standing at that door.

Shall I find comfort, travel-sore and weak?
   Of labour you shall find the sum.
Will there be beds for me and all who seek?
   Yea, beds for all who come.

—*Christina Rossetti*

Christina Rossetti (1830-1894), born in London to an Italian father and a half-Italian, half-English mother, was one of four children who would become distinguished in the arts in Victorian England. Like her brother Gabriel, whose work is also in this companion, Rossetti was educated at home by her parents. We can read this poem *literally*—as if it were describing a physical journey up a hill or mountain. Or the journey could be a metaphor. What in your life is like an uphill journey—a challenging undertaking that you hope will end in comfort and rest?

Brave Writer

Common Dust

And who shall separate the dust
What later we shall be:
Whose keen discerning eye will scan
And solve the mystery?

The high, the low, the rich, the poor,
The black, the white, the red,
And all the chromatique between,
Of whom shall it be said:

Here lies the dust of Africa;
Here are the sons of Rome;
Here lies the one unlabelled,
The world at large his home!

Can one then separate the dust?
Will mankind lie apart,
When life has settled back again
The same as from the start?

—*Georgia Douglas Johnson*

....

Georgia Douglas Johnson (1880–1966) was born in Atlanta, Georgia, to parents of African American, Native American, and English descent. She became a member of the Harlem Renaissance, the dynamic African-American cultural movement that followed World War I and emerged in the Harlem neighborhood of New York. Johnson's house in Washington, DC—the S Street Salon—was the site of open houses attended by other writers associated with the Harlem Renaissance (including Countee Cullen, who you will also find in our companion). What questions drive this poem? What answers does it suggest?

....

Brave Writer

Brave Writer

AUTUMN

Many words for this season mean "harvest," "end of summer," or even "under winter." The exact Latin origin of the word "autumn" isn't known, but in North America it goes by another, plainer name, contributed by city dwellers: fall.

Harvest is a time of bounty, reaping, and gathering. The time when leaves fall is also linked with impermanence, change, and letting go. Mist and mourning, dropping fruits and sighing winds. It's a time when the land prepares to sleep and welcome winter. These are some of the themes you can look for in this section.

Round

Hail to the merry Autumn days, when
yellow corn-fields shine,
Far brighter than the costly cup that
holds the monarch's wine!
Hail to the merry harvest time, the
gayest of the year,
The time of rich and bounteous crops,
rejoicing, and good cheer!

'Tis pleasant on a fine Spring morn to
see the buds expand,
'Tis pleasant in the Summer time to
view the teeming land;
'Tis pleasant on a Winter's night to
crouch around the blaze,—
But what are joys like these, my boys, to
Autumn's merry days!

Then hail to merry Autumn days, when
yellow corn-fields shine,
Far brighter than the costly cup that
holds the monarch's wine!
And hail to merry harvest time, the
gayest of the year,
The time of rich and bounteous crops,
rejoicing, and good cheer!

—*Charles Dickens*

If you've come across the tales of *Oliver Twist, A Christmas Carol, David Copperfield,* or *Great Expectations,* you already know that Charles Dickens (1812-1870) wrote some of the best-loved novels in English literature. Born in Portsmouth, England, Dickens left school at the age of 12 to work full-time in a factory in hopes of getting his family out of debtors' prison. In Victorian England, people who couldn't pay their bills were often sent to prison. The harsh working conditions and separation from his family that he endured affected Dickens for the rest of his life. This poem seems to celebrate an earlier, happier period in his childhood, or good times as the father of ten children! Here's something to try: list three things you love about your favorite season.

Brave Writer

Mist

Low-anchored cloud,
Newfoundland air,
Fountain-head and source of rivers,
Dew-cloth, dream-drapery,
And napkin spread by fays;
Drifting meadow of the air,
Where bloom the daisied banks and violets,
And in whose fenny labyrinth
The bittern booms and heron wades;
Spirit of lakes and seas and rivers, —
Bear only perfumes and the scent
Of healing herbs to just men's fields.

—Henry David Thoreau

••

Henry David Thoreau was born in Concord, Massachusetts in 1817. A neighbor of writers Ralph Waldo Emerson, the Alcott family (including Louisa May, author of *Little Women*), and Nathaniel Hawthorne, Thoreau was fortunate to live in a time and place full of interesting people and ideas. Two movements key to his development were the anti-slavery movement and American Transcendentalism. Thoreau loved to be outside and go for long walks. Where is your favorite place to walk?

••

Brave Writer

Dirge in Woods

A wind sways the pines,
    And below
Not a breath of wild air;
Still as the mosses that glow
On the flooring and over the lines
Of the roots here and there.
The pine-tree drops its dead;
They are quiet, as under the sea.
Overhead, overhead
Rushes life in a race,
As the clouds the clouds chase;
    And we go,
And we drop like the fruits of the tree,
    Even we,
    Even so.

—*George Meredith*

Born in Portsmouth, England, George Meredith (1828-1909) was equal parts novelist and poet. His novels are noted for their psychological studies of character and for putting forth the view that women are the equals of men—a rare theme for a male writer in Victorian England. This poem achieves a sense of stillness below while the wind rushes high overhead. A *dirge* is a song of mourning for the dead. Who is the poet singing this dirge for, in your opinion?

The Autumn

Go, sit upon the lofty hill,
And turn your eyes around,
Where waving woods and waters wild
Do hymn an autumn sound.
The summer sun is faint on them —
The summer flowers depart —
Sit still — as all transform'd to stone,
Except your musing heart.

How there you sat in summer-time,
May yet be in your mind;
And how you heard the green woods sing
Beneath the freshening wind.
Though the same wind now blows around,
You would its blast recall;
For every breath that stirs the trees,
Doth cause a leaf to fall.

Oh! like that wind, is all the mirth
That flesh and dust impart:
We cannot bear its visitings,
When change is on the heart.

Gay words and jests may make us smile,
When Sorrow is asleep;
But other things must make us smile,
When Sorrow bids us weep!

The dearest hands that clasp our hands, —
Their presence may be o'er;
The dearest voice that meets our ear,
That tone may come no more!
Youth fades; and then, the joys of youth,
Which once refresh'd our mind,
Shall come — as, on those sighing woods,
The chilling autumn wind.

Hear not the wind — view not the woods;
Look out o'er vale and hill —
In spring, the sky encircled them —
The sky is round them still.
Come autumn's scathe — come winter's cold —
Come change — and human fate!
Whatever prospect Heaven doth bound,
Can ne'er be desolate.

—Elizabeth Barrett Browning

Elizabeth Barrett Browning (1806–1861), born in Durham, England, was the eldest of 12 children. She started writing poetry when she was six years old, read voraciously and was self-taught in several languages. She became a successful, famous, and influential poet, and married the poet Robert Browning. The Barretts, her father's family, made their living from sugar plantations in Jamaica. This, and her own study of history and politics, led Barrett Browning to concern herself with social justice in her work.

Autumn Song

Know'st thou not at the fall of the leaf
How the heart feels a languid grief
    Laid on it for a covering,
    And how sleep seems a goodly thing
In Autumn at the fall of the leaf?

And how the swift beat of the brain
Falters because it is in vain,
    In Autumn at the fall of the leaf
    Knowest thou not? and how the chief
Of joys seems—not to suffer pain?

Know'st thou not at the fall of the leaf
How the soul feels like a dried sheaf
    Bound up at length for harvesting,
    And how death seems a comely thing
In Autumn at the fall of the leaf?

—*Dante Gabriel Rossetti*

Dante Gabriel Rossetti (1828–1882) was born into a London household governed by a love of politics and culture. He showed early promise as a poet and painter, and he and his three home-educated siblings would grow up to work in the arts. His sister Christina is in this companion, too. Gabriel, as he was called, was a founder of a group of artists and writers called the Pre-Raphaelite Brotherhood. How does the narrator of this poem describe his feelings during autumn? How do you feel during autumn?

Autumn

A touch of cold in the Autumn night—
I walked abroad,
And saw the ruddy moon lean over a hedge
Like a red-faced farmer.
I did not stop to speak, but nodded,
And round about were the wistful stars
With white faces like town children.

—T. E. Hulme

••

T. E. Hulme (1883-1917), born in Endon, Staffordshire, England, was thrown out of school for being too rowdy. He became a soldier and died in World War I. With H.D., also included in our companion, he founded the Imagist movement. Imagist poets sought to create sharp, precise pictures with words. What images can you find in this poem?

••

Brave Writer

CREATURES OF THE AIR

Here are poems about things with wings—some take to the air aggressively, others unsuccessfully. A poem itself feels like a creature of the air! You'll find butterflies and bees, predators and egg-layers, those who soar and those whose wings leave them grounded. Maybe as you read these poems you'll be inspired to write a poem addressed to a feathered friend!

The Eagle

He clasps the crag with crooked hands;
Close to the sun in lonely lands,
Ring'd with the azure world, he stands.

The wrinkled sea beneath him crawls;
He watches from his mountain walls,
And like a thunderbolt he falls.

—Alfred, Lord Tennyson

The poet laureate of Victorian England, Alfred, Lord Tennyson (1809-1892) was born in Somersby, Lincolnshire. The fourth of twelve children, he showed an early talent for writing. His family life was full of challenges, but Tennyson was happy in his years at Trinity College in Cambridge, where he made close friends that influenced his life and work. If you search online, you can find Thomas Edison's wax cylinder recording of Tennyson reading his poem, "The Charge of the Light Brigade." It's cool to hear the voice of a Victorian poet! Try going through the poem in our companion, "The Eagle," line by line: what picture does it paint? What do you learn about the eagle? What do you think happens after the last line of the poem?

True Royalty

There was never a Queen like Balkis,
From here to the wide world's end;
But Balkis talked to a butterfly
As you would talk to a friend.

There was never a King like Solomon,
Not since the world began;
But Solomon talked to a butterfly
As a man would talk to a man.

She was Queen of Sabaea—
And he was Asia's Lord—
But they both of 'em talked to butterflies
When they took their walks abroad.

—Rudyard Kipling

Though he was named for Rudyard Lake in Staffordshire England, where his parents became acquainted and decided to marry, Rudyard Kipling (1865-1936) was born in Bombay, India. He was sent back to England from ages 5 to 16 and lived in mostly miserable circumstances, but returned to India to work as a journalist for another period of years that greatly influenced his writing. He is known for *The Jungle Book* and *Kim*. This poem concludes "The Butterfly That Stamped" in Kipling's *Just So Stories for Little Children*. This poem draws a contrast between the lofty life of a king and queen and their habit, talking to butterflies, which introduces a note of whimsy. Can you make a poem that draws a similar contrast between something weighty and something fanciful?

Brave Writer

The Humble-Bee

Burly, dozing humble-bee,
Where thou art is clime for me.
Let them sail for Porto Rique,
Far-off heats through seas to seek;
I will follow thee alone,
Thou animated torrid-zone!
Zigzag steerer, desert cheerer,
Let me chase thy waving lines;
Keep me nearer, me thy hearer,
Singing over shrubs and vines.

Insect lover of the sun,
Joy of thy dominion!
Sailor of the atmosphere;
Swimmer through the waves of air;
Voyager of light and noon;
Epicurean of June;
Wait, I prithee, till I come
Within earshot of thy hum,—
All without is martyrdom.

When the south wind, in May days,
With a net of shining haze
Silvers the horizon wall,
And with softness touching all,
Tints the human countenance
With a color of romance,
And infusing subtle heats,
Turns the sod to violets,
Thou, in sunny solitudes,
Rover of the underwoods,
The green silence dost displace
With thy mellow, breezy bass.

Hot midsummer's petted crone,
Sweet to me thy drowsy tone
Tells of countless sunny hours,
Long days, and solid banks of flowers;
Of gulfs of sweetness without bound
In Indian wildernesses found;
Of Syrian peace, immortal leisure,
Firmest cheer, and bird-like pleasure.

Aught unsavory or unclean
Hath my insect never seen;
But violets and bilberry bells,
Maple-sap and daffodels,
Grass with green flag half-mast high,
Succory to match the sky,
Columbine with horn of honey,
Scented fern, and agrimony,
Clover, catchfly, adder's-tongue
And brier-roses, dwelt among;
All beside was unknown waste,
All was picture as he passed.

Wiser far than human seer,
Yellow-breeched philosopher!
Seeing only what is fair,
Sipping only what is sweet,
Thou dost mock at fate and care,
Leave the chaff, and take the wheat.
When the fierce northwestern blast
Cools sea and land so far and fast,
Thou already slumberest deep;
Woe and want thou canst outsleep;
Want and woe, which torture us,
Thy sleep makes ridiculous.

—Ralph Waldo Emerson

Ralph Waldo Emerson (1803-1882) lived in Concord, Massachusetts among a circle of writer-philosopher friends that included Margaret Fuller, Henry David Thoreau, Amos Bronson Alcott, and his daughter Louisa May Alcott. Known to us now as the American Transcendentalists, they promoted the idea that the meaning of life was to be found in individual experience, intuition, and time spent in nature. Emerson, a brilliant essayist, was its chief spokesperson. "Trust thyself" was his motto. The short lines of this poem give us a long meditation on the honey bee. Try counting the syllables in the lines of this poem. Are they all the same or do they vary? What do you notice about the rhyme pattern?

Winged Man

The moon, a sweeping scimitar, dipped in the stormy straits,
The dawn, a crimson cataract, burst through the eastern gates,
The cliffs were robed in scarlet, the sands were cinnabar,
Where first two men spread wings for flight and dared the hawk afar.

There stands the cunning workman, the crafty past all praise,
The man who chained the Minotaur, the man who built the Maze.
His young son is beside him and the boy's face is a light,
A light of dawn and wonder and of valor infinite.

Their great vans beat the cloven air, like eagles they mount up,
Motes in the wine of morning, specks in a crystal cup,
And lest his wings should melt apace old Daedalus flies low,
But Icarus beats up, beats up, he goes where lightnings go.

He cares no more for warnings, he rushes through the sky,
Braving the crags of ether, daring the gods on high,
Black 'gainst the crimson sunset, golden o'er cloudy snows,
With all Adventure in his heart the first winged man arose.

Dropping gold, dropping gold, where the mists of morning rolled,
On he kept his way undaunted, though his breaths were stabs of cold,
Through the mystery of dawning that no mortal may behold.

Now he shouts, now he sings in the rapture of his wings,
And his great heart burns intenser with the strength of his desire,
As he circles like a swallow, wheeling, flaming, gyre on gyre.

Gazing straight at the sun, half his pilgrimage is done,
And he staggers for a moment, hurries on, reels backward, swerves
In a rain of scattered feathers as he falls in broken curves.

Icarus, Icarus, though the end is piteous,
Yet forever, yea, forever we shall see thee rising thus,
See the first supernal glory, not the ruin hideous.

You were Man, you who ran farther than our eyes can scan,
Man absurd, gigantic, eager for impossible Romance,
Overthrowing all Hell's legions with one warped and broken lance.

On the highest steeps of Space he will have his dwelling-place,
In those far, terrific regions where the cold comes down like Death
Gleams the red glint of his pinions, smokes the vapor of his breath.

Floating downward, very clear, still the echoes reach the ear
Of a little tune he whistles and a little song he sings,
Mounting, mounting still, triumphant, on his torn and broken wings!

—*Stephen Vincent Benét*

Born into a military family in Bethlehem, Pennsylvania, Stephen Vincent Benét (1898-1943) is best known for his long Civil War poem, "John Brown's Body." Devoted to historical themes throughout his life, Benét co-authored with his wife Rosemary a book of poems about historical figures called *A Book of Americans*. In "Winged Man" he brings the Greek myth of Icarus to life. Icarus flew too close to the sun with wings made of feathers and wax. The wax melted in the heat and Icarus fell.

This poem is full of metaphors and similes (both ways of saying "this is like that"; an example of a metaphor is, "I'm a sneaky fox"; an example of a simile is "I'm as sneaky as a fox" or "I'm sneaky like a fox"). How many of these figures of speech can you find in this poem? Hint: the very first line contains a metaphor.

The Owl

Downhill I came, hungry, and yet not starved;
Cold, yet had heat within me that was proof
Against the North wind; tired, yet so that rest
Had seemed the sweetest thing under a roof.

Then at the inn I had food, fire, and rest,
Knowing how hungry, cold, and tired was I.
All of the night was quite barred out except
An owl's cry, a most melancholy cry

Shaken out long and clear upon the hill,
No merry note, nor cause of merriment,
But one telling me plain what I escaped
And others could not, that night, as in I went.

And salted was my food, and my repose,
Salted and sobered, too, by the bird's voice
Speaking for all who lay under the stars,
Soldiers and poor, unable to rejoice.

—*Edward Thomas*

Philip Edward Thomas (1878-1917) was born in London, England to Welsh parents. He was one of six children. His first book was a collection of essays called *The Woodland Life* (1896) about the long walks he liked to take. He began writing poetry at the urging of his good friend, Robert Frost, who wrote a poem you may know, "Stopping by Woods on a Snowy Evening." A few years later, World War I began. Thomas enlisted and died in the war. In his two years of being a solder he wrote 140 poems.

What do you think the narrator of "The Owl" means when he says his repose, or sleep, was "salted and sobered" by the voice of the owl?

The Hen

Alas, my Child, where is the Pen
That can do Justice to the Hen?
Like Royalty, She goes her way,
Laying foundations every day,
Though not for Public Buildings, yet
For Custard, Cake and Omelette.
Or if too Old for such a use
They have their Fling at some Abuse,
As when to Censure Plays Unfit
Upon the Stage they make a Hit,
Or at elections Seal the Fate
Of an Obnoxious Candidate.
No wonder, Child, we prize the Hen,
Whose Egg is mightier than the Pen.

—*Oliver Herford*

Oliver Herford (1863–1935) was a British-born American writer, artist and illustrator who published his work in very funny books with names like *The Bashful Earthquake* and *A Little Book of Bores*. He also had a talent for amusing one-liners, for example, "There is no time like the pleasant" or "Only the young die good." The laughs were all in the family: his sister, Beatrice Herford was also a humorist, and his wife, Margaret Regan, was a poet and playwright. In this poem, Herford imagines the hen as one who "lays foundations" for "building" custard, cake, and omelettes. Did you catch a pun in there? Can you come up with more puns about things animals do that are similar to things people do?

Brave Writer

WINTER

The ways of winter are catalogued, celebrated, and railed against in the poems that follow. One quality of winter we find here is its silence and stillness. There is beauty and the power to chill, desolation outside and a crackling hearth within. No doubt, winter days are best accompanied by tea, warm baked goods, and these poems!

When Icicles Hang by the Wall

When icicles hang by the wall,
And Dick the shepherd blows his nail,
And Tom bears logs into the hall,
And milk comes frozen home in pail,
When blood is nipp'd and ways be foul,
Then nightly sings the staring owl,
   Tu-whit; Tu-who,—
a merry note,
While greasy Joan doth keel the pot.

When all aloud the wind doth blow,
And coughing drowns the parson's saw,
And birds sit brooding in the snow,
And Marian's nose looks red and raw,
When roasted crabs hiss in the bowl,
Then nightly sings the staring owl,
   Tu-whit; Tu-who,—
a merry note,
While greasy Joan doth keel the pot.

—*William Shakespeare*

••

    The most widely read and performed playwright in the world, William Shakespeare (1564-1616) wrote 37 plays and more than 150 sonnets. He was born in Stratford-upon-Avon, but there are so many murky details in his life that people have gone so far as to argue that someone else is responsible for his plays and poems. How anyone could have produced the astounding body of work completed by William Shakespeare is an enduring mystery. This poem comes from the play *Love's Labour's Lost*. At the opening of this poem, a shepherd blows on the tips of his fingers to warm them. Can you tell the whole story of the poem? Can you hear the heartbeat of iambic pentameter in the lines as you read them aloud? Shakespeare was perhaps the greatest master of this rhythm.

••

Thirteen Ways of Looking at a Blackbird

I
Among twenty snowy mountains,
The only moving thing
Was the eye of the blackbird.

II
I was of three minds,
Like a tree
In which there are three blackbirds.

III
The blackbird whirled in the autumn winds.
It was a small part of the pantomime.

IV
A man and a woman
Are one.
A man and a woman and a blackbird
Are one.

V
I do not know which to prefer,
The beauty of inflections
Or the beauty of innuendoes,
The blackbird whistling
Or just after.

VI
Icicles filled the long window
With barbaric glass.
The shadow of the blackbird
Crossed it, to and fro.
The mood
Traced in the shadow
An indecipherable cause.

VII
O thin men of Haddam,
Why do you imagine golden birds?
Do you not see how the blackbird
Walks around the feet
Of the women about you?

VIII
I know noble accents
And lucid, inescapable rhythms;
But I know, too,
That the blackbird is involved
In what I know.

IX
When the blackbird flew out of sight,
It marked the edge
Of one of many circles.

X
At the sight of blackbirds
Flying in a green light,
Even the bawds of euphony
Would cry out sharply.

XI
He rode over Connecticut
In a glass coach.
Once, a fear pierced him,
In that he mistook
The shadow of his equipage
For blackbirds.

XII
The river is moving.
The blackbird must be flying.

XIII
It was evening all afternoon.
It was snowing
And it was going to snow.
The blackbird sat
In the cedar-limbs.

—*Wallace Stevens*

Wallace Stevens (1879-1955) moonlighted as a poet. By day, he was an executive at an insurance company, settling in Hartford, Connecticut for most of his career. Composing the bulk of his best-known work relatively late in life, Stevens became a major American poet and was awarded the Pulitzer Prize for Poetry for his Collected Poems in 1955. He died shortly thereafter. Stevens was born in Reading, Pennsylvania and educated at Harvard and New York Law School. You might notice that this poem is like a series of haikus, even if it doesn't strictly follow the rules of the form. You might like to try following, and changing, the rules of a haiku: compose a three-line poem with a total of seventeen syllables, broken into 5/7/5 for your three lines. A haiku typically focuses on an image from nature and is characterized by directness and simplicity. You can string many of them like Stevens did and make a longer poem.

A January Dandelion

All Nashville is a chill. And everywhere
Like desert sand, when the winds blow,
There is each moment sifted through the air,
A powdered blast of January snow.
O! thoughtless Dandelion, to be misled
By a few warm days to leave thy natural bed,
Was folly growth and blooming over soon.
And yet, thou blasted yellow-coated gem,
Full many a heart has but a common boon
With thee, now freezing on thy slender stem.
When the heart has bloomed by the touch of love's warm breath
Then left and chilling snow is sifted in,
It still may beat but there is blast and death
To all that blooming life that might have been.

—*George Marion McClellan*

Born in Belfast, Tennessee, George Marion McClellan (1860-1934) was a minister and teacher in addition to being a poet and writer. He received bachelor's and master's degrees from Fisk University, a historically African-American school whose celebrated graduates include the writer W. E. B. Dubois and the journalist, Ida B. Wells. McClellan also graduated from Hartford Theological Seminary with a bachelor of divinity degree. In this poem, McClellan draws a comparison between something in nature and a matter of the heart. What is happening outside in your world today and what in your life might you compare it to?

The Darkling Thrush

I leant upon a coppice gate
    When Frost was spectre-grey,
And Winter's dregs made desolate
    The weakening eye of day.
The tangled bine-stems scored the sky
    Like strings of broken lyres,
And all mankind that haunted nigh
    Had sought their household fires.

The land's sharp features seemed to be
    The Century's corpse outleant,
His crypt the cloudy canopy,
    The wind his death-lament.
The ancient pulse of germ and birth
    Was shrunken hard and dry,
And every spirit upon earth
    Seemed fervourless as I.

At once a voice arose among
    The bleak twigs overhead
In a full-hearted evensong
    Of joy illimited;
An aged thrush, frail, gaunt, and small,
    In blast-beruffled plume,
Had chosen thus to fling his soul
    Upon the growing gloom.

So little cause for carolings
    Of such ecstatic sound
Was written on terrestrial things
    Afar or nigh around,
That I could think there trembled through
    His happy good-night air
Some blessed Hope, whereof he knew
    And I was unaware.

—*Thomas Hardy*

Though he was a prolific and dedicated poet, Thomas Hardy (1840-1928) is better remembered today for his novels, which include *The Mayor of Casterbridge* and *Far from the Madding Crowd*. His home county of rural Dorset, England, inspired much of his work. He trained as an architect, but his growing fame as a novelist persuaded him to switch professions. See if you can make out the meaning of this poem before looking up any vocabulary words. What effect does it have on you when Hardy capitalizes a word?

Spellbound

The night is darkening round me,
The wild winds coldly blow;
But a tyrant spell has bound me
And I cannot, cannot go.

The giant trees are bending
Their bare boughs weighed with snow.
And the storm is fast descending,
And yet I cannot go.

Clouds beyond clouds above me,
Wastes beyond wastes below;
But nothing drear can move me;
I will not, cannot go.

—Emily Jane Brontë

Emily Jane Brontë (1818–1848) wrote her only novel, *Wuthering Heights*, under the pen name Ellis Bell. She and her sisters Anne and Charlotte began writing when they were young and wrote some of the best-known novels of the Victorian era. The speaker in this poem finds herself unable to move. "Spellbound" means to be held as if in a trance. Can you remember being spellbound by winter? What can you remember about it?

Brave Writer

SOLITUDE

You could spend a lifetime reading poems about solitude. It's ironic that poets work alone but write in order to connect with a reader. The poems in this section celebrate time alone in nature, getting quiet, listening to the voices inside us. Being alone isn't the same as being lonely, at least not always. Time away from other people, in most of these poems, is a kind of vacation, a way to rest, a sojourn that leads us back into community with others. What do you do when you are alone? Where do you go? What are the gifts of solitude? Think about your own answers to these questions as you read these poems.

Have you got a brook in your little heart

Have you got a brook in your little heart,
Where bashful flowers blow,
And blushing birds go down to drink,
And shadows tremble so?

And nobody knows, so still it flows,
That any brook is there;
And yet your little draught of life
Is daily drunken there.

Then look out for the little brook in March,
When the rivers overflow,
And the snows come hurrying from the hills,
And the bridges often go.

And later, in August it may be,
When the meadows parching lie,
Beware, lest this little brook of life
Some burning noon go dry!

—*Emily Dickinson*

••

Emily Dickinson (1830-1886) wasn't well known during her lifetime, but she is known today as one of America's greatest poets and an innovator with a voice uniquely her own. She was most comfortable in her Amherst family home and entertained few visitors, but she loved to write letters and she read widely. She made her poems into booklets of paper sheets she sewed together. Do you have a brook in your little heart? What kinds of events are like the floods of March for your brook and what kinds of events are like the dry heat of August? (Note to our friends in the Southern Hemisphere: you may need to translate these to months appropriate to your climate!)

••

A Fantasy

Her voice is like clear water
That drips upon a stone
In forests far and silent
Where Quiet plays alone.

Her thoughts are like the lotus
Abloom by sacred streams
Beneath the temple arches
Where Quiet sits and dreams.

Her kisses are the roses
That glow while dusk is deep
In Persian garden closes
Where Quiet falls asleep.

—*Sara Teasdale*

Born in St. Louis, Missouri, and homeschooled until the age of 9 for health reasons, Sara Teasdale (1884–1933) frequently visited Chicago and, as an adult, moved to New York City. She published seven volumes of poetry and won the Columbia University Poetry Society Prize, which became the Pulitzer Prize for Poetry. In this poem, "Quiet" is a person. How would you describe her? You might draw her portrait as she plays in the forest, dreams beneath the temple arches, or sleeps in the garden. Or think of your own special place and imagine what Quiet is doing there.

I Wandered Lonely as a Cloud

I wandered lonely as a cloud
That floats on high o'er vales and hills,
When all at once I saw a crowd,
A host, of golden daffodils;
Beside the lake, beneath the trees,
Fluttering and dancing in the breeze.

Continuous as the stars that shine
And twinkle on the milky way,
They stretched in never-ending line
Along the margin of a bay:
Ten thousand saw I at a glance,
Tossing their heads in sprightly dance.

The waves beside them danced; but they
Out-did the sparkling waves in glee:
A poet could not but be gay,
In such a jocund company:
I gazed—and gazed—but little thought
What wealth the show to me had brought:

For oft, when on my couch I lie
In vacant or in pensive mood,
They flash upon that inward eye
Which is the bliss of solitude;
And then my heart with pleasure fills,
And dances with the daffodils.

—William Wordsworth

....

William Wordsworth (1770–1850) was born in 1770, in Cockermouth, Cumberland, England. He was an orphan at the age of 13. He studied at grammar school and Cambridge University, and became a founder of the Romantic movement in England. Romanticism, the main artistic movement of the late 18th century, is characterized by a belief in the importance of passion, self-reliance, a love of nature, and an interest in mind and spirit. Can you find examples of any of these in this poem?

....

Afternoon on a Hill

I will be the gladdest thing
    Under the sun!
I will touch a hundred flowers
    And not pick one.

I will look at cliffs and clouds
    With quiet eyes,
Watch the wind bow down the grass,
    And the grass rise.

And when lights begin to show
    Up from the town,
I will mark which must be mine,
    And then start down!

—Edna St. Vincent Millay

Edna St. Vincent Millay (1892-1950) was born in Rockland, Maine. Her mother raised her and her two sisters in an environment that placed a high value on literature and art. Millay, known to her friends as "Vincent," studied piano and theater and learned six languages. She won the Pulitzer Prize in 1923. The rhyme scheme of this short-lined poem sticks out. How many syllables can you count in each line? What rhyming words can you find?

The Lake Isle of Innisfree

I will arise and go now, and go to Innisfree,
And a small cabin build there, of clay and wattles made;
Nine bean-rows will I have there, a hive for the honey-bee,
And live alone in the bee-loud glade.

And I shall have some peace there, for peace comes dropping slow,
Dropping from the veils of the morning to where the cricket sings;
There midnight's all a glimmer, and noon a purple glow,
And evening full of the linnet's wings.

I will arise and go now, for always night and day
I hear lake water lapping with low sounds by the shore;
While I stand on the roadway, or on the pavements grey,
I hear it in the deep heart's core.

—William Butler Yeats

• •

William Butler Yeats (1865–1939), born in Sandymount, Ireland and educated there and in London, is considered one of the great figures of British 20th-century literature. The committee of the Nobel Prize in Literature, which made him the first Irishman to attain that honor, described his work as "inspired poetry, which in a highly artistic form gives expression to the spirit of a whole nation." The folklore of Ireland was a big influence in his work. As you read this poem, what do you notice about the rhyme scheme?

• •

Brave Writer

SPRING

The world over, spring is a symbol of creation, birth, or rebirth. This section begins with a poem about the four elements: fire, earth, air, and water. In Classical Greece and in many other thought traditions, the elements formed the world. People also linked the elements to the four directions and the four seasons.

Spring is a time of beginnings, of rain and flowers, of love's first stirrings. It's a time to look ahead, a good time to start something. Think about the many meanings of "spring" as you read these poems. What will you start today?

The Four Elements *[excerpt]*

The Fire, Air, Earth and water did contest
Which was the strongest, noblest and the best,
Who was of greatest use and might'est force;
In placide Terms they thought now to discourse,
That in due order each her turn should speak;
But enmity this amity did break
All would be chief, and all scorn'd to be under
Whence issu'd winds & rains, lightning & thunder
The quaking earth did groan, the Sky lookt black
The Fire, the forced Air, in sunder crack;
The sea did threat the heav'ns, the heavn's the earth,
All looked like a Chaos or new birth:
Fire broyled Earth, & scorched Earth it choaked

Both by their darings, water so provoked
That roaring in it came, and with its source
Soon made the Combatants abate their force
The rumbling hissing, puffing was so great
The worlds confusion, it did seem to threat
Till gentle Air, Contention so abated
That betwixt hot and cold, she arbitrated
The others difference, being less did cease
All storms now laid, and they in perfect peace
That Fire should first begin, the rest consent,
The noblest and most active Element.

—*Anne Bradstreet*

Anne Bradstreet (1612–1672), born in Northampton, England, came by ship with her family to Massachusetts. She was a prominent English poet of North America, the first female writer in the colonies to be published, and the first female poet to be published both in England and the New World. Well-educated thanks to being tutored in many subjects, Bradstreet married at 16. Both her father and husband served as governors of the Massachusetts Bay Colony and both were founders of Harvard University. This is the beginning of a poem that imagines a throw-down among the four elements. Which one do you think will win and why?

I Have a Rendezvous with Life

I have a rendezvous with Life,
In days I hope will come,
Ere youth has sped, and strength of mind,
Ere voices sweet grow dumb.
I have a rendezvous with Life,
When Spring's first heralds hum.
Sure some would cry it's better far
To crown their days with sleep
Than face the road, the wind and rain,
To heed the calling deep.
Though wet nor blow nor space I fear,
Yet fear I deeply, too,
Lest Death should meet and claim me ere
I keep Life's rendezvous.

—Countee Cullen

Countee Cullen (1903-1946) grew up in a Methodist parsonage in New York City, graduated from New York University and Harvard University, and became a leader of the Harlem Renaissance. In addition to being a poet, he was a novelist, playwright, children's author, and high school teacher. Cullen wrote this poem while he was still in high school, as a response to another poem, "I Have a Rendezvous with Death," by Alan Seeger. The archaic word "ere" that Cullen used in this poem means "soon" or "before" and is related to the words "early" and "erstwhile." A rendezvous is a meeting. What kinds of rendezvous do you have coming up in your life?

Beloved, Let Us Once More Praise the Rain

Beloved, let us once more praise the rain.
Let us discover some new alphabet,
For this, the often praised; and be ourselves,
The rain, the chickweed, and the burdock leaf,
The green-white privet flower, the spotted stone,
And all that welcomes the rain; the sparrow too,—
Who watches with a hard eye from seclusion,
Beneath the elm-tree bough, till rain is done.
There is an oriole who, upside down,
Hangs at his nest, and flicks an orange wing,—
Under a tree as dead and still as lead;
There is a single leaf, in all this heaven
Of leaves, which rain has loosened from its twig:
The stem breaks, and it falls, but it is caught
Upon a sister leaf, and thus she hangs;
There is an acorn cup, beside a mushroom
Which catches three drops from the
    stooping cloud.
The timid bee goes back to the hive; the fly
Under the broad leaf of the hollyhock
Perpends stupid with cold; the raindark snail
Surveys the wet world from a watery stone...
And still the syllables of water whisper:
The wheel of cloud whirs slowly: while we wait
In the dark room; and in your heart I find
One silver raindrop,—on a hawthorn leaf,—
Orion in a cobweb, and the World.

—*Conrad Potter Aiken*

Conrad Potter Aiken (1889-1973) was born in Savannah, Georgia, to parents who came from New England. While he was still very young, his parents died and he returned to New England to be raised by a family member. Over a period of nearly fifty years, Aiken published poems, essays, short stories, novels, and literary criticism. Among his many honors, he was U.S. Poet Laureate from 1950-1952. This poem is a marvel of collected detail. Whether it's raining during your teatime or not, have a look and see what's outside your window. See if you can make a list. You could even use Aiken's structure and fill in the blanks:

Let us discover…

There is a…

Under a…

The Red Wheelbarrow

so much depends
upon

a red wheel
barrow

glazed with rain
water

beside the white
chickens

—*William Carlos Williams*

Born in Rutherford, New Jersey, William Carlos Williams (1883-1963) was not only a revolutionary poet, he was a doctor for more than 40 years, practicing medicine by day and writing at night. Like Ezra Pound and Hilda Doolittle, with whom he was friends, he was part of a poetry movement called Imagism. He also loved painting. What about this poem, if anything, reminds you of a painting? When you read this poem and then close your eyes, what image do you see?

Brave Writer

Song On May Morning

Now the bright morning Star, Dayes harbinger,
Comes dancing from the East, and leads with her
The Flowry May, who from her green lap throws
The yellow Cowslip, and the pale Primrose.
Hail bounteous May that dost inspire
Mirth and youth, and warm desire,
Woods and Groves, are of thy dressing,
Hill and Dale, doth boast thy blessing.
Thus we salute thee with our early Song,
And welcom thee, and wish thee long.

—*John Milton*

Born in London, John Milton (1608-1674) abandoned his plans to become a priest in the Church of England in order to become a poet. He is famous for writing what is commonly considered the greatest epic poem of the English language, *Paradise Lost*, a retelling of the Bible story of Genesis in blank (unrhymed) verse. By the time he wrote it he was blind and wrote by dictating his words to a transcriber. He also asked his daughters to read aloud to him. Maybe you have someone who transcribes for you and reads to you!

Although Milton grew to dislike rhyme, he uses it in this poem to create a series of couplets (rhyming lines of verse in pairs). He also dresses his poem in a *conceit* or *extended metaphor* (a metaphor is one way of saying one thing is like another, for example, "blanket of snow").

How does Milton describe the morning star and the month of May? It may help you to know that a "harbinger" is one who makes an announcement.

A Red, Red Rose

O my Luve is like a red, red rose
   That's newly sprung in June;
O my Luve is like the melody
   That's sweetly played in tune.

So fair art thou, my bonnie lass,
   So deep in luve am I;
And I will luve thee still, my dear,
   Till a' the seas gang dry.

Till a' the seas gang dry, my dear,
   And the rocks melt wi' the sun;
O I will love thee still, my dear,
   While the sands o' life shall run.

And fare thee weel, my only luve!
   And fare thee weel awhile!
And I will come again, my luve,
   Though it were ten thousand mile.

—*Robert Burns*

Robert Burns (1759–1796), born in Scotland to a farming family, came to be known as "the Scottish Bard." He was a prolific writer of poems and songs, and if you sing "Auld Lang Syne" on New Year's Eve (called Hogmanay in Scotland), you are singing his work. Burns was also known as "the people's poet," because the lot of the common person was a frequent theme in his work. Without looking up the Scots words in this poem, see if you can figure out what they mean! You might also like to learn the tune and sing this one.

Brave Writer

Brave Writer

CREATURES OF LAND AND WATER

Poems about animals ignite a sense of wonder about the diversity of creatures in our world. They often ask us to consider how human features surface in other animals. A patient spider, a singing grasshopper, a sensitive frog, a placid pug, a phlegmatic shark, and a "kindly" crocodile are the characters you are about to meet. Be careful you don't get tea up your nose laughing!